S0-BDS-824

THE INSECT GOD

by Edward Gorey

BEAUFORT BOOKS
PUBLISHERS
NEW YORK

Library of Congress Catalog Card Number: 63-13763
Published in the United States by Beaufort Books Publishers
Printed in the United States
First Beaufort Edition
0-8253-0396-6

For Sylvia

O what has become of Millicent Frastley?
Is there any hope that she's still alive?
Why haven't they found her? It's rather ghastly
To think that the child was not yet five.

The dear little thing was last seen playing
Alone by herself at the edge of the park;
There was no one with her to keep her from straying
Away in the shadows and oncoming dark.

Before she could do so, a silent and glittering
Black motor drew up where she sat nibbling grass;
From within came a nearly inaudible twittering,
A tiny green face peered out through the glass.

She was ready to flee, when the figure beckoned;
An arm with two elbows held out a tin
Full of cinnamon balls; she paused; a second
Reached out as she took one, and lifted her in.

The nurse was discovered collapsed in some shrubbery,
But her reappearance was not much use;
Her eyes were askew, her extremities rubbery,
Her clothing was stained with a brownish juice.

She was questioned in hopes of her answers revealing
What had happened; she merely repeatedly said
'I hear them walking about on the ceiling'.
She had gone irretrievably out of her head.

O feelings of horror, resentment, and pity
For things, which so seldom turn out for the best:
The car, unobserved, sped away from the city
As the last of the light died out in the west.

The Frastleys grew sick with apprehension,
Which a heavy tea only served to increase;
Though they felt it was scarcely genteel to mention
The loss of their child, they called in the police.

Through unvisited hamlets the car went creeping,
With its head lamps unlit and its curtains drawn;
Those natives who happened not to be sleeping
Heard it pass, and lay awake until dawn.

The police with their torches and notebooks descended
On the haunts of the underworld, looking for clues;
In spite of their praiseworthy efforts, they ended
With nothing at all in the way of news.

The car, after hours and hours of travel,
Arrived at a gate in an endless wall;
It rolled up a drive and stopped on the gravel
At the foot of a vast and crumbling hall.

As the night wore away hope started to languish
And soon was replaced by all manner of fears;
The family twisted their fingers in anguish,
Or got them all damp from the flow of their tears.

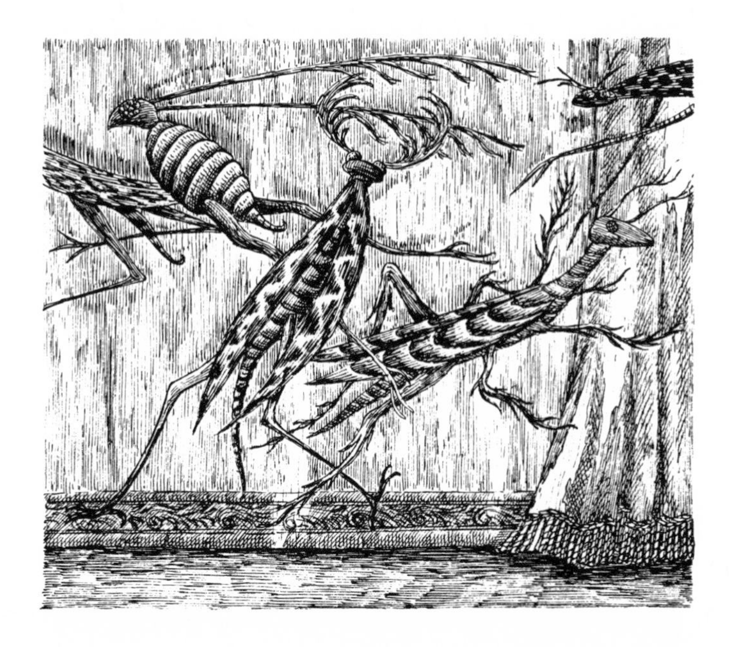

They removed the child to the ball-room, whose hangings
And mirrors were streaked with a luminous slime;
They leapt through the air with buzzings and twangings
To work themselves up to a ritual crime.

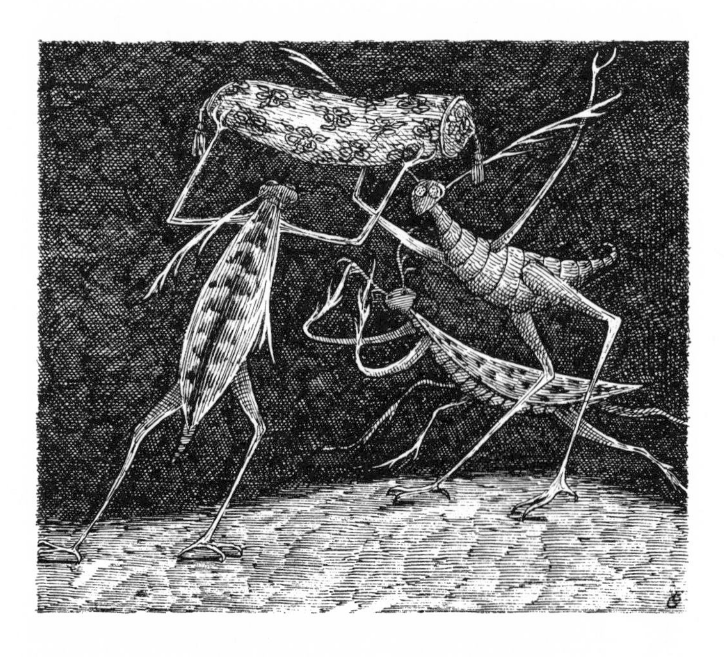

They stunned her, and stripped off her garments, and lastly
They stuffed her inside a kind of pod;
And then it was that Millicent Frastley
Was sacrificed to THE INSECT GOD.